Fuck it
2023 Planner
for Sarcastically Gifted Women

Sassy Quotes Press

You are fucking amazing

And you need a planner that really gets that. One that's funny, fun to use and will help you get shit done.

Strong women use strong language!
Language that's as creative and colorful as you are and helps you deal with assholes and bullshit.

This planner is filled with motivational swear quotes and affirmations to help you laugh and stay positive as fuck.

You'll also find gratitude prompts and checklists to make sure you're saving your fucks for important shit.

All in a clear, easy-to-use format that will help you stay focused and avoid shitshows.

So drop those fbombs! Let those fucks fly! Be your awesome self!

And enjoy the kickass year you deserve.

Starting. Right. Fucking. Now.

Sign up for freebies, prize giveaways and updates at **SassyQuotesPress.com**

This belongs to

2023

January

S	M	T	W	T	F	S
1	2	3	4	5	6	7
8	9	10	11	12	13	14
15	16	17	18	19	20	21
22	23	24	25	26	27	28
29	30	31				

February

S	M	T	W	T	F	S
			1	2	3	4
5	6	7	8	9	10	11
12	13	14	15	16	17	18
19	20	21	22	23	24	25
26	27	28				

March

S	M	T	W	T	F	S
			1	2	3	4
5	6	7	8	9	10	11
12	13	14	15	16	17	18
19	20	21	22	23	24	25
26	27	28	29	30	31	

April

S	M	T	W	T	F	S
						1
2	3	4	5	6	7	8
9	10	11	12	13	14	15
16	17	18	19	20	21	22
23	24	25	26	27	28	29
30						

May

S	M	T	W	T	F	S
	1	2	3	4	5	6
7	8	9	10	11	12	13
14	15	16	17	18	19	20
21	22	23	24	25	26	27
28	29	30	31			

June

S	M	T	W	T	F	S
				1	2	3
4	5	6	7	8	9	10
11	12	13	14	15	16	17
18	19	20	21	22	23	24
25	26	27	28	29	30	

July

S	M	T	W	T	F	S
						1
2	3	4	5	6	7	8
9	10	11	12	13	14	15
16	17	18	19	20	21	22
23	24	25	26	27	28	29
30	31					

August

S	M	T	W	T	F	S
		1	2	3	4	5
6	7	8	9	10	11	12
13	14	15	16	17	18	19
20	21	22	23	24	25	26
27	28	29	30	31		

September

S	M	T	W	T	F	S
					1	2
3	4	5	6	7	8	9
10	11	12	13	14	15	16
17	18	19	20	21	22	23
24	25	26	27	28	29	30

October

S	M	T	W	T	F	S
1	2	3	4	5	6	7
8	9	10	11	12	13	14
15	16	17	18	19	20	21
22	23	24	25	26	27	28
29	30	31				

November

S	M	T	W	T	F	S
			1	2	3	4
5	6	7	8	9	10	11
12	13	14	15	16	17	18
19	20	21	22	23	24	25
26	27	28	29	30		

December

S	M	T	W	T	F	S
					1	2
3	4	5	6	7	8	9
10	11	12	13	14	15	16
17	18	19	20	21	22	23
24	25	26	27	28	29	30
31						

2024

January

S	M	T	W	T	F	S
	1	2	3	4	5	6
7	8	9	10	11	12	13
14	15	16	17	18	19	20
21	22	23	24	25	26	27
28	29	30	31			

February

S	M	T	W	T	F	S
				1	2	3
4	5	6	7	8	9	10
11	12	13	14	15	16	17
18	19	20	21	22	23	24
25	26	27	28	29		

March

S	M	T	W	T	F	S
					1	2
3	4	5	6	7	8	9
10	11	12	13	14	15	16
17	18	19	20	21	22	23
24	25	26	27	28	29	30
31						

April

S	M	T	W	T	F	S
	1	2	3	4	5	6
7	8	9	10	11	12	13
14	15	16	17	18	19	20
21	22	23	24	25	26	27
28	29	30				

May

S	M	T	W	T	F	S
			1	2	3	4
5	6	7	8	9	10	11
12	13	14	15	16	17	18
19	20	21	22	23	24	25
26	27	28	29	30	31	

June

S	M	T	W	T	F	S
						1
2	3	4	5	6	7	8
9	10	11	12	13	14	15
16	17	18	19	20	21	22
23	24	25	26	27	28	29
30						

July

S	M	T	W	T	F	S
	1	2	3	4	5	6
7	8	9	10	11	12	13
14	15	16	17	18	19	20
21	22	23	24	25	26	27
28	29	30	31			

August

S	M	T	W	T	F	S
				1	2	3
4	5	6	7	8	9	10
11	12	13	14	15	16	17
18	19	20	21	22	23	24
25	26	27	28	29	30	31

September

S	M	T	W	T	F	S
1	2	3	4	5	6	7
8	9	10	11	12	13	14
15	16	17	18	19	20	21
22	23	24	25	26	27	28
29	30					

October

S	M	T	W	T	F	S
	1	2	3	4	5	
6	7	8	9	10	11	12
13	14	15	16	17	18	19
20	21	22	23	24	25	26
27	28	29	30	31		

November

S	M	T	W	T	F	S
					1	2
3	4	5	6	7	8	9
10	11	12	13	14	15	16
17	18	19	20	21	22	23
24	25	26	27	28	29	30

December

S	M	T	W	T	F	S
1	2	3	4	5	6	7
8	9	10	11	12	13	14
15	16	17	18	19	20	21
22	23	24	25	26	27	28
29	30	31				

Goals & shit

What goals do you want to crush with your awesomeness? Self care, relationships, hobbies, work? Your possibilities are endless.

_____

_____

_____

_____

_____

_____

_____

_____

_____

_____

_____

_____

_____

_____

_____

_____

_____

_____

_____

_____

Insults & Comebacks

You don't have time for assholes! With this handy cheat sheet, you can put them in their place and keep going. There's room to add more favorites.

I'll never forget the first time we met. But I'll keep fucking trying.

Seeing you reminds me... I need to get more "Bitch-B-Gone."

It's a beautiful day to leave me the fuck alone.

I'm busy right now. Can I tell you to fuck off another time?

I've been called worse things by better bitches.

You have your whole life to be an asshole. Why not take the day off?

Your best shot at getting laid is to crawl up a chicken's ass and wait.

I can explain it to you, but I can't fucking understand it for you.

Were you born this fucking stupid or did you take lessons?

If I wanted to hear from an asshole, I'd fart.

The people who tolerate your shit on a daily basis are the real heroes.

Good story, but in what chapter do you shut the fuck up?

You're so full of shit, you make toilets jealous.

In order to insult me, I must first value your opinion.

Being a dick won't make yours any bigger.

I love the sound you make when you shut the fuck up.

I'm sorry I hurt your feelings when I called you an asshole. I thought you already knew.

It's okay if you fucking disagree with me. I can't force you to be right.

Hating me doesn't make you pretty.

If you listen closely, you can hear me not caring.

You should carry a plant around with you to replace the oxygen you waste.

You look like a million I-don't-give-a-fucks.

If you find me offensive, then I suggest you stop fucking finding me.

I'm not insulting you. I'm describing you.

You're about as useful as a knitted condom.

_____

_____

_____

_____

_____

December 2022-January 2023

Important as **fuck**

Fucking grateful for...

Happy Fucking New Year!

29 THURSDAY

_____
_____
_____
_____
_____
_____
_____
_____
_____
_____
_____
○ _____
○ _____
○ _____
○ _____
○ _____
○ _____
○ _____
○ _____
○ _____

30 FRIDAY

_____
_____
_____
_____
_____
_____
_____
_____
_____
_____
_____
○ _____
○ _____
○ _____
○ _____
○ _____
○ _____
○ _____
○ _____
○ _____

31 SATURDAY
New Year's Eve

_____
_____
_____
_____
_____
○ _____
○ _____
○ _____

1 SUNDAY
New Year's Day

_____
_____
_____
_____
_____
○ _____
○ _____
○ _____

Notes and shit

_____
_____
_____

JANUARY 2023

Sunday	Monday	Tuesday	Wednesday
1 New Year's Day	2	3	4
8	9	10	11
15	16 Martin Luther King Jr. Day (US)	17	18
22 Chinese New Year	23	24	25
29	30	31	

Dear 2023, Don't be an asshole

Thursday	Friday	Saturday	Important **shit**
5	6	7	_____ _____ _____ _____ _____
12	13	14	_____ _____ _____ _____ _____
19	20	21	_____ _____ _____ _____ _____
26	27 International Holocaust Remembrance Day	28	_____ _____ _____ _____

December 2022

S	M	T	W	T	F	S
				1	2	3
4	5	6	7	8	9	10
11	12	13	14	15	16	17
18	19	20	21	22	23	24
25	26	27	28	29	30	31

February

S	M	T	W	T	F	S
			1	2	3	4
5	6	7	8	9	10	11
12	13	14	15	16	17	18
19	20	21	22	23	24	25
26	27	28				

January 2023

2 MONDAY	3 TUESDAY	4 WEDNESDAY
_____	_____	_____
_____	_____	_____
_____	_____	_____
_____	_____	_____
_____	_____	_____
_____	_____	_____
_____	_____	_____
_____	_____	_____
_____	_____	_____
_____	_____	_____
_____	_____	_____
_____	_____	_____
_____	_____	_____
○ _____	○ _____	○ _____
○ _____	○ _____	○ _____
○ _____	○ _____	○ _____
○ _____	○ _____	○ _____
○ _____	○ _____	○ _____
○ _____	○ _____	○ _____
○ _____	○ _____	○ _____
○ _____	○ _____	○ _____
○ _____	○ _____	○ _____

Important as **fuck**

Fucking grateful for...

_____

_____

_____

_____

You give off that Boss Bitch energy

5 THURSDAY

_____
_____
_____
_____
_____
_____
_____
_____
_____
_____
_____
_____
○ _____
○ _____
○ _____
○ _____
○ _____
○ _____
○ _____
○ _____
○ _____

6 FRIDAY

_____
_____
_____
_____
_____
_____
_____
_____
_____
_____
_____
○ _____
○ _____
○ _____
○ _____
○ _____
○ _____
○ _____
○ _____
○ _____

7 SATURDAY

_____
_____
_____
_____
_____
○ _____
○ _____
○ _____

8 SUNDAY

_____
_____
_____
_____
○ _____
○ _____
○ _____

Notes and shit

_____
_____
_____

January 2023

9 MONDAY	10 TUESDAY	11 WEDNESDAY

Important as fuck

Fucking grateful for...

Giving a fuck doesn't really go with your outfit

12 THURSDAY

_____
_____
_____
_____
_____
_____
_____
_____
_____
_____
_____
_____
_____

- ○ _____
- ○ _____
- ○ _____
- ○ _____
- ○ _____
- ○ _____
- ○ _____
- ○ _____
- ○ _____

13 FRIDAY

_____
_____
_____
_____
_____
_____
_____
_____
_____
_____
_____

- ○ _____
- ○ _____
- ○ _____
- ○ _____
- ○ _____
- ○ _____
- ○ _____
- ○ _____
- ○ _____

14 SATURDAY

_____
_____
_____
_____
_____
- ○ _____
- ○ _____
- ○ _____

15 SUNDAY

_____
_____
_____
_____
_____
_____
- ○ _____
- ○ _____
- ○ _____

Notes and shit

_____
_____
_____

January 2023

16 MONDAY
Martin Luther King Jr. Day (US)

_____
_____
_____
_____
_____
_____
_____
_____
_____
_____
_____
_____

○ _____
○ _____
○ _____
○ _____
○ _____
○ _____
○ _____
○ _____
○ _____

17 TUESDAY

_____
_____
_____
_____
_____
_____
_____
_____
_____
_____
_____
_____

○ _____
○ _____
○ _____
○ _____
○ _____
○ _____
○ _____
○ _____
○ _____

18 WEDNESDAY

_____
_____
_____
_____
_____
_____
_____
_____
_____
_____
_____
_____

○ _____
○ _____
○ _____
○ _____
○ _____
○ _____
○ _____
○ _____
○ _____

Important as **fuck**

_____
_____
_____

Fucking grateful for...

_____
_____
_____

Self care is the best middle finger you can ever give

19 THURSDAY

_____
_____
_____
_____
_____
_____
_____
_____
_____
_____
_____

○ _____
○ _____
○ _____
○ _____
○ _____
○ _____
○ _____
○ _____
○ _____

20 FRIDAY

_____
_____
_____
_____
_____
_____
_____
_____
_____
_____

○ _____
○ _____
○ _____
○ _____
○ _____
○ _____
○ _____
○ _____
○ _____

21 SATURDAY

_____
_____
_____
_____
_____
_____
○ _____
○ _____
○ _____

22 SUNDAY
Chinese New Year

_____
_____
_____
_____
○ _____
○ _____
○ _____

Notes and shit

_____
_____
_____

January 2023

23 MONDAY	24 TUESDAY	25 WEDNESDAY

Important as **fuck**

Fucking grateful for...

"Fuck this shit" is a perfectly fine way to say "No"

26 THURSDAY

27 FRIDAY
International Holocaust Remembrance Day

28 SATURDAY

- ○
- ○
- ○

29 SUNDAY

- ○
- ○
- ○
- ○
- ○
- ○
- ○
- ○
- ○

- ○
- ○
- ○
- ○
- ○
- ○
- ○
- ○
- ○

- ○
- ○
- ○

Notes and shit

FEBRUARY 2023

Sunday	Monday	Tuesday	Wednesday
			1
5	6	7	8
12	13	14 Valentine's Day	15
19	20 Presidents' Day (US)	21	22 Ash Wednesday
26	27	28	

You're too glam to give a damn

Thursday	Friday	Saturday	Important **shit**
2	3	4	_____
			_____
			_____
Groundhog Day (US)			_____
9	10	11	_____
			_____
			_____
16	17	18	_____
			_____
			_____
23	24	25	_____

January

S	M	T	W	T	F	S
1	2	3	4	5	6	7
8	9	10	11	12	13	14
15	16	17	18	19	20	21
22	23	24	25	26	27	28
29	30	31				

March

S	M	T	W	T	F	S
			1	2	3	4
5	6	7	8	9	10	11
12	13	14	15	16	17	18
19	20	21	22	23	24	25
26	27	28	29	30	31	

January-February 2023

30 MONDAY	31 TUESDAY	1 WEDNESDAY
_____	_____	_____
_____	_____	_____
_____	_____	_____
_____	_____	_____
_____	_____	_____
_____	_____	_____
_____	_____	_____
_____	_____	_____
_____	_____	_____
_____	_____	_____
_____	_____	_____
○ _____	○ _____	○ _____
○ _____	○ _____	○ _____
○ _____	○ _____	○ _____
○ _____	○ _____	○ _____
○ _____	○ _____	○ _____
○ _____	○ _____	○ _____
○ _____	○ _____	○ _____
○ _____	○ _____	○ _____
○ _____	○ _____	○ _____

Important as **fuck**

Fucking grateful for...

Honest question: Do you ever get tired of being so fucking awesome?

2 THURSDAY
Groundhog Day

_____
_____
_____
_____
_____
_____
_____
_____
_____
_____
_____
_____

- ○ _____
- ○ _____
- ○ _____
- ○ _____
- ○ _____
- ○ _____
- ○ _____
- ○ _____
- ○ _____

3 FRIDAY

_____
_____
_____
_____
_____
_____
_____
_____
_____
_____
_____
_____

- ○ _____
- ○ _____
- ○ _____
- ○ _____
- ○ _____
- ○ _____
- ○ _____
- ○ _____
- ○ _____

4 SATURDAY

_____
_____
_____
_____
_____
_____
- ○ _____
- ○ _____
- ○ _____

5 SUNDAY

_____
_____
_____
_____
_____
_____
- ○ _____
- ○ _____
- ○ _____

Notes and shit

_____
_____
_____

February 2023

6 MONDAY	7 TUESDAY	8 WEDNESDAY

_____
_____
_____
_____
_____
_____
_____
_____
_____
_____
_____
_____

○ _____
○ _____
○ _____
○ _____
○ _____
○ _____
○ _____
○ _____
○ _____

Important as fuck

_____
_____
_____

Fucking grateful for...

_____
_____
_____

Real bitches are never perfect and perfect bitches are never real

9 THURSDAY

_____
_____
_____
_____
_____
_____
_____
_____
_____
_____
_____
_____
_____

- ○ _____
- ○ _____
- ○ _____
- ○ _____
- ○ _____
- ○ _____
- ○ _____
- ○ _____
- ○ _____

10 FRIDAY

_____
_____
_____
_____
_____
_____
_____
_____
_____
_____
_____
_____
_____

- ○ _____
- ○ _____
- ○ _____
- ○ _____
- ○ _____
- ○ _____
- ○ _____
- ○ _____
- ○ _____

11 SATURDAY

_____
_____
_____
_____
_____

- ○ _____
- ○ _____
- ○ _____

12 SUNDAY

_____
_____
_____
_____
_____

- ○ _____
- ○ _____
- ○ _____

Notes and shit

_____
_____
_____

February 2023

A wise woman once said...

13 MONDAY

14 TUESDAY
Valentine's Day

15 WEDNESDAY

Important as **fuck**

Fucking grateful for...

"Fuck this shit!" and lived happily ever after

16 THURSDAY

_____
_____
_____
_____
_____
_____
_____
_____
_____
_____
_____
_____
○ _____
○ _____
○ _____
○ _____
○ _____
○ _____
○ _____
○ _____
○ _____

17 FRIDAY

_____
_____
_____
_____
_____
_____
_____
○ _____
○ _____
○ _____
○ _____
○ _____
○ _____
○ _____
○ _____
○ _____

18 SATURDAY

_____
_____
_____
_____
_____
○ _____
○ _____
○ _____

19 SUNDAY

_____
_____
_____
_____
○ _____
○ _____
○ _____

Notes and **shit**

_____
_____
_____

February 2023

20 MONDAY
Presidents' Day (US)

_____
_____
_____
_____
_____
_____
_____
_____
_____
_____
_____
_____
_____

- ⭕ _____
- ⭕ _____
- ⭕ _____
- ⭕ _____
- ⭕ _____
- ⭕ _____
- ⭕ _____
- ⭕ _____
- ⭕ _____

21 TUESDAY

_____
_____
_____
_____
_____
_____
_____
_____
_____
_____
_____
_____
_____

- ⭕ _____
- ⭕ _____
- ⭕ _____
- ⭕ _____
- ⭕ _____
- ⭕ _____
- ⭕ _____
- ⭕ _____
- ⭕ _____

22 WEDNESDAY
Ash Wednesday

_____
_____
_____
_____
_____
_____
_____
_____
_____
_____
_____
_____
_____

- ⭕ _____
- ⭕ _____
- ⭕ _____
- ⭕ _____
- ⭕ _____
- ⭕ _____
- ⭕ _____
- ⭕ _____
- ⭕ _____

Important as **fuck**

_____
_____
_____

Fucking grateful for...

_____
_____
_____

Forgive assholes. They hate that.

23 THURSDAY

_____
_____
_____
_____
_____
_____
_____
_____
_____
_____
_____
_____

○ _____
○ _____
○ _____
○ _____
○ _____
○ _____
○ _____
○ _____
○ _____

24 FRIDAY

_____
_____
_____
_____
_____
_____
_____
_____

○ _____
○ _____
○ _____
○ _____
○ _____
○ _____
○ _____
○ _____
○ _____

25 SATURDAY

_____
_____
_____
_____
_____
_____
○ _____
○ _____
○ _____

26 SUNDAY

_____
_____
_____
_____
_____
_____
○ _____
○ _____
○ _____

Notes and **shit**

_____
_____
_____

MARCH 2023

Sunday	Monday	Tuesday	Wednesday

February
S M T W T F S
        1 2 3 4
5 6 7 8 9 10 11
12 13 14 15 16 17 18
19 20 21 22 23 24 25
26 27 28
	April
	S M T W T F S
	                1
	2 3 4 5 6 7 8
	9 10 11 12 13 14 15
	16 17 18 19 20 21 22
	23 24 25 26 27 28 29
	30
			1

5	**6** Purim begins at sundown	**7**	**8** International Women's Day
12 Daylight Saving Time begins	**13**	**14**	**15**
19 Mother's Day (UK)	**20** Spring begins	**21**	**22** First of Ramadan begins at sundown
26	**27**	**28**	**29**

Fuck-eddaboutit!

Thursday	Friday	Saturday	Important **shit**
2	3	4	
9	10	11	
16	17 St. Patrick's Day	18	
23	24	25	
30	31		

February-March 2023

27 MONDAY	28 TUESDAY	1 WEDNESDAY

Important as **fuck**

Fucking grateful for...

To thine own self be fucking true. ~William Fucking Shakespeare

2 THURSDAY

_____
_____
_____
_____
_____
_____
_____
_____
_____
_____
_____
○ _____
○ _____
○ _____
○ _____
○ _____
○ _____
○ _____
○ _____
○ _____

3 FRIDAY

_____
_____
_____
_____
_____
_____
_____
_____
_____
_____
_____
○ _____
○ _____
○ _____
○ _____
○ _____
○ _____
○ _____
○ _____
○ _____

4 SATURDAY

_____
_____
_____
_____
_____
○ _____
○ _____
○ _____

5 SUNDAY

_____
_____
_____
_____
_____
○ _____
○ _____
○ _____

Notes and shit

_____
_____
_____

March 2023

May you never reach a point when...

6 MONDAY
Purim begins at sundown

7 TUESDAY

8 WEDNESDAY
International Women's Day

Important as **fuck**

Fucking grateful for...

you need a stronger word than "Fuck!"

9 THURSDAY

10 FRIDAY

11 SATURDAY

- ○
- ○
- ○

12 SUNDAY
Daylight Saving Time begins

○
○
○
○
○
○
○
○
○

○
○
○
○
○
○
○
○
○

○
○
○

Notes and **shit**

March 2023

13 MONDAY	14 TUESDAY	15 WEDNESDAY

Important as **fuck**

Fucking grateful for...

Seize the fucking day

16 THURSDAY

_____
_____
_____
_____
_____
_____
_____
_____
_____
_____
_____
_____

○ _____
○ _____
○ _____
○ _____
○ _____
○ _____
○ _____
○ _____
○ _____

17 FRIDAY
St. Patrick's Day

_____
_____
_____
_____
_____
_____
_____
_____

○ _____
○ _____
○ _____
○ _____
○ _____
○ _____
○ _____
○ _____
○ _____

18 SATURDAY

_____
_____
_____
_____
○ _____
○ _____
○ _____

19 SUNDAY

_____
_____
_____
_____
○ _____
○ _____
○ _____

Notes and shit

_____
_____
_____

March 2023

20 MONDAY
Spring begins

_____
_____
_____
_____
_____
_____
_____
_____
_____
_____
_____
_____

- ○ _____
- ○ _____
- ○ _____
- ○ _____
- ○ _____
- ○ _____
- ○ _____
- ○ _____
- ○ _____

21 TUESDAY

_____
_____
_____
_____
_____
_____
_____
_____
_____
_____
_____
_____

- ○ _____
- ○ _____
- ○ _____
- ○ _____
- ○ _____
- ○ _____
- ○ _____
- ○ _____
- ○ _____

22 WEDNESDAY
First of Ramadan begins at sundown

_____
_____
_____
_____
_____
_____
_____
_____
_____
_____
_____
_____

- ○ _____
- ○ _____
- ○ _____
- ○ _____
- ○ _____
- ○ _____
- ○ _____
- ○ _____
- ○ _____

Important as **fuck**

_____
_____
_____

Fucking grateful for...

_____
_____
_____

Sometimes life's a bitch. That's okay, you're fluent in bitch.

23 THURSDAY

_____
_____
_____
_____
_____
_____
_____
_____
_____
_____
_____
_____

○ _____
○ _____
○ _____
○ _____
○ _____
○ _____
○ _____
○ _____
○ _____

24 FRIDAY

_____
_____
_____
_____
_____
_____
_____
_____
_____
_____

○ _____
○ _____
○ _____
○ _____
○ _____
○ _____
○ _____
○ _____
○ _____

25 SATURDAY

_____
_____
_____
_____
_____

○ _____
○ _____
○ _____

26 SUNDAY

_____
_____
_____
_____
_____

○ _____
○ _____
○ _____

Notes and **shit**

_____
_____
_____

APRIL 2023

Sunday	Monday	Tuesday	Wednesday
2 Palm Sunday	3	4	5 Passover starts at sundown
9 Easter	10 Easter Monday	11	12
16	17	18	19
23 St. George's Day (UK)	24	25	26 Administrative Professionals Day
30			

It's a beautiful day to get shit done

Thursday	Friday	Saturday	Important **shit**
		1 April Fools' Day	_____ _____ _____ _____
6	7 Good Friday	8	_____ _____ _____
13	14	15	_____ _____ _____ _____
20	21 (Eid) al Fitr begins at sundown	22 Earth Day, Victoria Day (CA)	_____ _____ _____ _____
27	28	29	_____ _____

March

S	M	T	W	T	F	S
			1	2	3	4
5	6	7	8	9	10	11
12	13	14	15	16	17	18
19	20	21	22	23	24	25
26	27	28	29	30	31	

May

S	M	T	W	T	F	S
	1	2	3	4	5	6
7	8	9	10	11	12	13
14	15	16	17	18	19	20
21	22	23	24	25	26	27
28	29	30	31			

March-April 2023

27 MONDAY	28 TUESDAY	29 WEDNESDAY

Important as **fuck**

Fucking grateful for...

You can't swear *all* the time. You have to sleep too.

30 THURSDAY

_____
_____
_____
_____
_____
_____
_____
_____
_____
_____
_____

- ○ _____
- ○ _____
- ○ _____
- ○ _____
- ○ _____
- ○ _____
- ○ _____
- ○ _____
- ○ _____

31 FRIDAY

_____
_____
_____
_____
_____
_____
_____
_____
_____
_____
_____

- ○ _____
- ○ _____
- ○ _____
- ○ _____
- ○ _____
- ○ _____
- ○ _____
- ○ _____
- ○ _____

1 SATURDAY
April Fools' Day

_____
_____
_____
_____
- ○ _____
- ○ _____
- ○ _____

2 SUNDAY
Palm Sunday

_____
_____
_____
_____
- ○ _____
- ○ _____
- ○ _____

Notes and shit

_____
_____
_____

April 2023

3 MONDAY	4 TUESDAY	5 WEDNESDAY
		Passover begins at sundown

_____
_____
_____
_____
_____
_____
_____
_____
_____
_____
_____
_____
_____

○ _____
○ _____
○ _____
○ _____
○ _____
○ _____
○ _____
○ _____
○ _____

Important as **fuck**

_____
_____
_____

Fucking grateful for...

_____
_____
_____

Don't stumble over shit that's behind you

6 THURSDAY

_____
_____
_____
_____
_____
_____
_____
_____
_____
_____
_____
_____

- ○ _____
- ○ _____
- ○ _____
- ○ _____
- ○ _____
- ○ _____
- ○ _____
- ○ _____
- ○ _____

7 FRIDAY
Good Friday

_____
_____
_____
_____
_____
_____
_____
_____
_____
_____

- ○ _____
- ○ _____
- ○ _____
- ○ _____
- ○ _____
- ○ _____
- ○ _____
- ○ _____
- ○ _____

8 SATURDAY

_____
_____
_____
_____
_____
- ○ _____
- ○ _____
- ○ _____

9 SUNDAY
Easter

_____
_____
_____
_____
_____
- ○ _____
- ○ _____
- ○ _____

Notes and **shit**

_____
_____
_____

April 2023

You're proof that it's possible to be a...

10 MONDAY	11 TUESDAY	12 WEDNESDAY
Easter Monday		

Important as fuck

Fucking grateful for...

fucking masterpiece and a work in progress at the same time

13 THURSDAY	14 FRIDAY	15 SATURDAY
_____	_____	_____
_____	_____	_____
_____	_____	_____
_____	_____	_____
_____	_____	_____
_____	_____	○ _____
_____	_____	○ _____
_____	_____	○ _____

16 SUNDAY

_____	_____	_____
_____	_____	_____
○ _____	○ _____	_____
○ _____	○ _____	_____
○ _____	○ _____	_____
○ _____	○ _____	_____
○ _____	○ _____	_____
○ _____	○ _____	○ _____
○ _____	○ _____	○ _____
○ _____	○ _____	○ _____

Notes and **shit**

_____

_____

April 2023

17 MONDAY	18 TUESDAY	19 WEDNESDAY

Important as **fuck**

Fucking grateful for...

looks aren't everything, bitch... but you have them just in case

20 THURSDAY

_____
_____
_____
_____
_____
_____
_____
_____
_____
_____
_____
_____

○ _____
○ _____
○ _____
○ _____
○ _____
○ _____
○ _____
○ _____
○ _____

21 FRIDAY
(Eid) al Fitr begins at sundown

_____
_____
_____
_____
_____
_____
_____
_____
_____
_____
_____

○ _____
○ _____
○ _____
○ _____
○ _____
○ _____
○ _____
○ _____
○ _____

22 SATURDAY
Earth Day, Victoria Day (Canada)

_____
_____
_____
_____
_____
○ _____
○ _____
○ _____

23 SUNDAY
St. George's Day (UK)

_____
_____
_____
_____
○ _____
○ _____
○ _____

Notes and shit

_____
_____
_____

April 2023

24 MONDAY

25 TUESDAY

26 WEDNESDAY
Administrative Professionals Day

Important as **fuck**

Fucking grateful for...

life is short. Make every middle finger count.

27 THURSDAY

_____
_____
_____
_____
_____
_____
_____
_____
_____
_____
_____
_____

○ _____
○ _____
○ _____
○ _____
○ _____
○ _____
○ _____
○ _____
○ _____

28 FRIDAY

_____
_____
_____
_____
_____
_____
_____
_____
_____
_____
_____

○ _____
○ _____
○ _____
○ _____
○ _____
○ _____
○ _____
○ _____
○ _____

29 SATURDAY

_____
_____
_____
_____
_____
○ _____
○ _____
○ _____

30 SUNDAY

_____
_____
_____
_____
_____
○ _____
○ _____
○ _____

Notes and shit

_____
_____
_____

MAY 2023

Sunday	Monday	Tuesday	Wednesday
	1 Early May Bank (UK), May Day	2	3
7	8	9	10
14 Mother's Day (US, CA)	15	16	17
21	22 Victoria Day (CA)	23	24
28	29 Memorial Day (US), Spring Bank Holiday (UK)	30	31

Master the art of not giving a fuck

Thursday	Friday	Saturday	Important shit
4	5	6	
	Cinco de Mayo (US)		
11	12	13	
18	19	20	
		Armed Forces Day (US)	
25	26	27	

April
S	M	T	W	T	F	S
						1
2	3	4	5	6	7	8
9	10	11	12	13	14	15
16	17	18	19	20	21	22
23	24	25	26	27	28	29
30						

June
S	M	T	W	T	F	S
				1	2	3
4	5	6	7	8	9	10
11	12	13	14	15	16	17
18	19	20	21	22	23	24
25	26	27	28	29	30	

May 2023

1 MONDAY
May Day, Early May Bank Holiday (UK)

_____
_____
_____
_____
_____
_____
_____
_____
_____
_____
_____
_____

○ _____
○ _____
○ _____
○ _____
○ _____
○ _____
○ _____
○ _____
○ _____

2 TUESDAY

_____
_____
_____
_____
_____
_____
_____
_____
_____
_____
_____
_____

○ _____
○ _____
○ _____
○ _____
○ _____
○ _____
○ _____
○ _____
○ _____

3 WEDNESDAY

_____
_____
_____
_____
_____
_____
_____
_____
_____
_____
_____
_____

○ _____
○ _____
○ _____
○ _____
○ _____
○ _____
○ _____
○ _____
○ _____

Important as **fuck**

_____
_____
_____

Fucking grateful for...

_____
_____
_____

The first five days after the weekend are the hardest

4 THURSDAY

_____
_____
_____
_____
_____
_____
_____
_____
_____
_____
_____
_____
○ _____
○ _____
○ _____
○ _____
○ _____
○ _____
○ _____
○ _____
○ _____

5 FRIDAY
Cinco de Mayo (US)

_____
_____
_____
_____
_____
_____
_____
_____
_____
_____
_____
_____
○ _____
○ _____
○ _____
○ _____
○ _____
○ _____
○ _____
○ _____
○ _____

6 SATURDAY

_____
_____
_____
_____
_____
○ _____
○ _____
○ _____

7 SUNDAY

_____
_____
_____
_____
○ _____
○ _____
○ _____

Notes and shit

_____
_____
_____

May 2023

8 MONDAY	9 TUESDAY	10 WEDNESDAY

Important as **fuck**

Fucking grateful for...

Inhale the good shit. Exhale the bullshit.

11 THURSDAY

_____
_____
_____
_____
_____
_____
_____
_____
_____
_____
_____
_____

○ _____
○ _____
○ _____
○ _____
○ _____
○ _____
○ _____
○ _____
○ _____

12 FRIDAY

_____
_____
_____
_____
_____
_____
_____
_____
_____

○ _____
○ _____
○ _____
○ _____
○ _____
○ _____
○ _____
○ _____
○ _____

13 SATURDAY

_____
_____
_____
_____
_____
○ _____
○ _____
○ _____

14 SUNDAY
Mother's Day (US, CA)

_____
_____
_____
_____
_____
○ _____
○ _____
○ _____

Notes and shit

_____
_____
_____

May 2023

There's a word for women like you....

15 MONDAY   16 TUESDAY   17 WEDNESDAY

Important as **fuck**

Fucking grateful for...

Ambitchous (adj.) - Having the attitude to reach higher altitude.

18 THURSDAY

_____
_____
_____
_____
_____
_____
_____
_____
_____
_____
_____
_____

○ _____
○ _____
○ _____
○ _____
○ _____
○ _____
○ _____
○ _____
○ _____

19 FRIDAY

_____
_____
_____
_____
_____
_____
_____
_____
_____
_____

○ _____
○ _____
○ _____
○ _____
○ _____
○ _____
○ _____
○ _____
○ _____

20 SATURDAY
Armed Forces Day

_____
_____
_____
_____
_____
○ _____
○ _____
○ _____

21 SUNDAY

_____
_____
_____
_____
_____
○ _____
○ _____
○ _____

Notes and shit

_____
_____
_____

May 2023

Important as **fuck**

Fucking grateful for...

You are fucking beautiful... inside and out

25 THURSDAY

_____
_____
_____
_____
_____
_____
_____
_____
_____
_____
_____
_____
_____

○ _____
○ _____
○ _____
○ _____
○ _____
○ _____
○ _____
○ _____
○ _____

26 FRIDAY

_____
_____
_____
_____
_____
_____
_____
_____
_____
_____
_____

○ _____
○ _____
○ _____
○ _____
○ _____
○ _____
○ _____
○ _____
○ _____

27 SATURDAY

_____
_____
_____
_____
_____
_____
○ _____
○ _____
○ _____

28 SUNDAY

_____
_____
_____
_____
_____
○ _____
○ _____
○ _____

Notes and shit

_____
_____
_____

JUNE 2023

Sunday	Monday	Tuesday	Wednesday
May S M T W T F S 　1　2　3　4　5　6 7　8　9　10　11　12　13 14　15　16　17　18　19　20 21　22　23　24　25　26　27 28　29　30　31	**July** S M T W T F S 　　　　　　1 2　3　4　5　6　7　8 9　10　11　12　13　14　15 16　17　18　19　20　21　22 23　24　25　26　27　28　29 30　31		
4	5	6	7
11	12	13	14 Flag Day (US)
18 Father's Day	19 Juneteenth (US)	20	21 Summer begins
25	26	27	28 (Eid) al Adha begins at sundown

let your dreams be your fucking wings

Thursday	Friday	Saturday	Important **shit**
1	2	3	
8	9	10 Queen's Birthday (UK)	
15	16	17	
22	23	24	
29	30		

May-June 2023

29 MONDAY
Memorial Day, Spring Bank Holiday (UK)

30 TUESDAY

31 WEDNESDAY

○
○
○
○
○
○
○
○
○

○
○
○
○
○
○
○
○
○

○
○
○
○
○
○
○
○
○

Important as **fuck**

Fucking grateful for...

You spread joy everywhere you go. Keep that shit up.

1 THURSDAY

_____
_____
_____
_____
_____
_____
_____
_____
_____
_____
_____
- ○ _____
- ○ _____
- ○ _____
- ○ _____
- ○ _____
- ○ _____
- ○ _____
- ○ _____
- ○ _____

2 FRIDAY

_____
_____
_____
_____
_____
_____
_____
_____
_____
_____
- ○ _____
- ○ _____
- ○ _____
- ○ _____
- ○ _____
- ○ _____
- ○ _____
- ○ _____
- ○ _____

3 SATURDAY

_____
_____
_____
_____
_____
- ○ _____
- ○ _____
- ○ _____

4 SUNDAY

_____
_____
_____
_____
- ○ _____
- ○ _____
- ○ _____

Notes and shit

_____
_____
_____

June 2023

5 MONDAY   6 TUESDAY   7 WEDNESDAY

Important as **fuck**

Fucking grateful for...

Do more of what makes you fucking happy

8 THURSDAY

_____
_____
_____
_____
_____
_____
_____
_____
_____
_____
_____
_____
_____
○ _____
○ _____
○ _____
○ _____
○ _____
○ _____
○ _____
○ _____
○ _____

9 FRIDAY

_____
_____
_____
_____
_____
_____
_____
_____
_____
_____
_____
_____
_____
○ _____
○ _____
○ _____
○ _____
○ _____
○ _____
○ _____
○ _____
○ _____

10 SATURDAY
Queen's birthday (UK)

_____
_____
_____
_____
_____
_____
○ _____
○ _____
○ _____

11 SUNDAY

_____
_____
_____
_____
_____
○ _____
○ _____
○ _____

Notes and shit

_____
_____
_____

June 2023

Flag Day (US)

Important as **fuck**

Fucking grateful for...

The shit that makes you different is the shit that makes you awesome

15 THURSDAY

_____
_____
_____
_____
_____
_____
_____
_____
_____
_____
_____

○ _____
○ _____
○ _____
○ _____
○ _____
○ _____
○ _____
○ _____
○ _____

16 FRIDAY

_____
_____
_____
_____
_____
_____
_____
_____
_____
_____

○ _____
○ _____
○ _____
○ _____
○ _____
○ _____
○ _____
○ _____
○ _____

17 SATURDAY

_____
_____
_____
_____
_____

○ _____
○ _____
○ _____

18 SUNDAY
Father's Day (US)

_____
_____
_____
_____

○ _____
○ _____
○ _____

Notes and shit

_____
_____
_____

June 2023

19 MONDAY	20 TUESDAY	21 WEDNESDAY
Juneteenth (US)		Summer begins

Important as **fuck**

Fucking grateful for...

Tell negative thoughts to fuck off

22 THURSDAY

_____
_____
_____
_____
_____
_____
_____
_____
_____
_____
_____

- ○ _____
- ○ _____
- ○ _____
- ○ _____
- ○ _____
- ○ _____
- ○ _____
- ○ _____
- ○ _____

23 FRIDAY

_____
_____
_____
_____
_____
_____
_____
_____
_____
_____
_____

- ○ _____
- ○ _____
- ○ _____
- ○ _____
- ○ _____
- ○ _____
- ○ _____
- ○ _____
- ○ _____

24 SATURDAY

_____
_____
_____
_____
_____
- ○ _____
- ○ _____
- ○ _____

25 SUNDAY

_____
_____
_____
_____
_____

- ○ _____
- ○ _____
- ○ _____

Notes and shit

_____
_____
_____

JULY 2023

Sunday	Monday	Tuesday	Wednesday
2	3	4 Independence Day (US)	5
9	10	11	12
16	17	18 First of Muharram begins at sundown	19
23	24	25	26
30	31		

Even in the summer, you're chill as fuck

Thursday	Friday	Saturday	Important **shit**
		1 Canada Day (CA)	
6	7	8	
13	14	15	
20	21	22	
27	28	29	

June

S	M	T	W	T	F	S
				1	2	3
4	5	6	7	8	9	10
11	12	13	14	15	16	17
18	19	20	21	22	23	24
25	26	27	28	29	30	

August

S	M	T	W	T	F	S
		1	2	3	4	5
6	7	8	9	10	11	12
13	14	15	16	17	18	19
20	21	22	23	24	25	26
27	28	29	30	31		

June-July 2023

Important as **fuck**

Fucking grateful for...

The only fucking approval that matters is your own

29 THURSDAY

30 FRIDAY

1 SATURDAY
Canada Day (CA)

- ○
- ○
- ○

2 SUNDAY

29 THURSDAY
- ○
- ○
- ○
- ○
- ○
- ○
- ○
- ○
- ○

30 FRIDAY
- ○
- ○
- ○
- ○
- ○
- ○
- ○
- ○
- ○

2 SUNDAY
- ○
- ○
- ○

Notes and shit

July 2023

3 MONDAY

4 TUESDAY
Independence Day (US)

5 WEDNESDAY

_____
_____
_____
_____
_____
_____
_____
_____
_____
_____
_____

○ _____
○ _____
○ _____
○ _____
○ _____
○ _____
○ _____
○ _____
○ _____

Important as **fuck**

Fucking grateful for...

_____
_____
_____

You swear because you care

_____
_____
_____
_____
_____
_____
_____
_____

○ _____
○ _____
○ _____

○ _____   ○ _____
○ _____   ○ _____
○ _____   ○ _____
○ _____   ○ _____
○ _____   ○ _____
○ _____   ○ _____
○ _____   ○ _____   ○ _____
○ _____   ○ _____   ○ _____
○ _____   ○ _____   ○ _____

Notes and **shit**

_____
_____
_____

July 2023

10 MONDAY	11 TUESDAY	12 WEDNESDAY

Important as **fuck**

Fucking grateful for...

You are a ray of fucking sunshine

13 THURSDAY

_____
_____
_____
_____
_____
_____
_____
_____
_____
_____
_____

○ _____
○ _____
○ _____
○ _____
○ _____
○ _____
○ _____
○ _____
○ _____

14 FRIDAY

_____
_____
_____
_____
_____
_____
_____
_____
_____
_____

○ _____
○ _____
○ _____
○ _____
○ _____
○ _____
○ _____
○ _____
○ _____

15 SATURDAY

_____
_____
_____
_____
_____
_____
○ _____
○ _____
○ _____

16 SUNDAY

_____
_____
_____
_____
○ _____
○ _____
○ _____

Notes and shit

_____
_____
_____

July 2023

Important as **fuck**

Fucking grateful for...

You are the rainbow after the shitstorm

20 THURSDAY

_____
_____
_____
_____
_____
_____
_____
_____
_____
_____
_____
_____

- ○ _____
- ○ _____
- ○ _____
- ○ _____
- ○ _____
- ○ _____
- ○ _____
- ○ _____
- ○ _____

21 FRIDAY

_____
_____
_____
_____
_____
_____
_____
_____
_____
_____

- ○ _____
- ○ _____
- ○ _____
- ○ _____
- ○ _____
- ○ _____
- ○ _____
- ○ _____
- ○ _____

22 SATURDAY

_____
_____
_____
_____
_____
- ○ _____
- ○ _____
- ○ _____

23 SUNDAY

_____
_____
_____
_____
_____
_____
- ○ _____
- ○ _____
- ○ _____

Notes and shit

_____
_____
_____

July 2023

Don't worry what assholes think...

24 MONDAY	25 TUESDAY	26 WEDNESDAY

Important as **fuck**

Fucking grateful for...

Thinking is not one of their strengths.

27 THURSDAY

_____
_____
_____
_____
_____
_____
_____
_____
_____
_____
_____
_____

○ _____
○ _____
○ _____
○ _____
○ _____
○ _____
○ _____
○ _____
○ _____

28 FRIDAY

_____
_____
_____
_____
_____
_____
_____
_____
_____
_____
_____

○ _____
○ _____
○ _____
○ _____
○ _____
○ _____
○ _____
○ _____
○ _____

29 SATURDAY

_____
_____
_____
_____
_____
_____
○ _____
○ _____
○ _____

30 SUNDAY

_____
_____
_____
_____
_____
○ _____
○ _____
○ _____

Notes and shit

_____
_____
_____

AUGUST 2023

Sunday	Monday	Tuesday	Wednesday

July
S M T W T F S
           1
2 3 4 5 6 7 8
9 10 11 12 13 14 15
16 17 18 19 20 21 22
23 24 25 26 27 28 29
30 31
	September
	S M T W T F S
	         1 2
	3 4 5 6 7 8 9
	10 11 12 13 14 15 16
	17 18 19 20 21 22 23
	24 25 26 27 28 29 30
		1	2

6	7 Civic Holiday (Canada)	8	9
13	14	15	16
20	21	22	23
27	28 Summer Bank Holiday (UK)	29	30

Make yourself a fucking priority

Thursday	Friday	Saturday	Important **shit**
3	4	5	_____
10	11	12	_____
17	18	19	_____
24	25	26	_____
31			_____

July-August 2023

31 MONDAY   1 TUESDAY   2 WEDNESDAY

_____   _____   _____
_____   _____   _____
_____   _____   _____
_____   _____   _____
_____   _____   _____
_____   _____   _____
_____   _____   _____
_____   _____   _____
_____   _____   _____
_____   _____   _____
_____   _____   _____
_____   _____   _____
_____   _____   _____

- ◯ _____   ◯ _____   ◯ _____
- ◯ _____   ◯ _____   ◯ _____
- ◯ _____   ◯ _____   ◯ _____
- ◯ _____   ◯ _____   ◯ _____
- ◯ _____   ◯ _____   ◯ _____
- ◯ _____   ◯ _____   ◯ _____
- ◯ _____   ◯ _____   ◯ _____
- ◯ _____   ◯ _____   ◯ _____
- ◯ _____   ◯ _____   ◯ _____

Important as **fuck**   **Fucking** grateful for...

_____   _____
_____   _____
_____   _____

Your inner critic is a total bitch. Ignore her.

3 THURSDAY

_____
_____
_____
_____
_____
_____
_____
_____
_____
_____
_____
_____
- ○ _____
- ○ _____
- ○ _____
- ○ _____
- ○ _____
- ○ _____
- ○ _____
- ○ _____
- ○ _____

4 FRIDAY

_____
_____
_____
_____
_____
_____
_____
_____
_____
_____
- ○ _____
- ○ _____
- ○ _____
- ○ _____
- ○ _____
- ○ _____
- ○ _____
- ○ _____
- ○ _____

5 SATURDAY

_____
_____
_____
_____
- ○ _____
- ○ _____
- ○ _____

6 SUNDAY

_____
_____
_____
_____
_____
- ○ _____
- ○ _____
- ○ _____

Notes and shit

_____
_____
_____

August 2023

Important as **fuck**

Fucking grateful for...

Keep your head high and your middle finger higher

13 SUNDAY

Notes and shit

August 2023

14 MONDAY	15 TUESDAY	16 WEDNESDAY
_____	_____	_____
_____	_____	_____
_____	_____	_____
_____	_____	_____
_____	_____	_____
_____	_____	_____
_____	_____	_____
_____	_____	_____
_____	_____	_____
_____	_____	_____
_____	_____	_____
_____	_____	_____

- ○ _____
- ○ _____
- ○ _____
- ○ _____
- ○ _____
- ○ _____
- ○ _____
- ○ _____
- ○ _____

Important as **fuck**

Fucking grateful for...

_____

_____

_____

Do epic shit. And, yes, epic naps count.

17 THURSDAY

_____
_____
_____
_____
_____
_____
_____
_____
_____
_____
_____

- ○ _____
- ○ _____
- ○ _____
- ○ _____
- ○ _____
- ○ _____
- ○ _____
- ○ _____
- ○ _____

18 FRIDAY

_____
_____
_____
_____
_____
_____
_____
_____
_____
_____
_____

- ○ _____
- ○ _____
- ○ _____
- ○ _____
- ○ _____
- ○ _____
- ○ _____
- ○ _____
- ○ _____

19 SATURDAY

_____
_____
_____
_____

- ○ _____
- ○ _____
- ○ _____

20 SUNDAY

_____
_____
_____
_____

- ○ _____
- ○ _____
- ○ _____

Notes and shit

_____
_____

August 2023

Kill them with kindness...

21 MONDAY

_____
_____
_____
_____
_____
_____
_____
_____
_____
_____
_____

- ○ _____
- ○ _____
- ○ _____
- ○ _____
- ○ _____
- ○ _____
- ○ _____
- ○ _____
- ○ _____

22 TUESDAY

_____
_____
_____
_____
_____
_____
_____
_____
_____
_____
_____

- ○ _____
- ○ _____
- ○ _____
- ○ _____
- ○ _____
- ○ _____
- ○ _____
- ○ _____
- ○ _____

23 WEDNESDAY

_____
_____
_____
_____
_____
_____
_____
_____
_____
_____
_____

- ○ _____
- ○ _____
- ○ _____
- ○ _____
- ○ _____
- ○ _____
- ○ _____
- ○ _____
- ○ _____

Important as **fuck**

_____
_____
_____

Fucking grateful for...

_____
_____
_____

Or torture them with sarcasm. You have options.

24 THURSDAY

_____
_____
_____
_____
_____
_____
_____
_____
_____
_____
_____
_____

- ○ _____
- ○ _____
- ○ _____
- ○ _____
- ○ _____
- ○ _____
- ○ _____
- ○ _____
- ○ _____

25 FRIDAY

_____
_____
_____
_____
_____
_____
_____
_____
_____
_____
_____

- ○ _____
- ○ _____
- ○ _____
- ○ _____
- ○ _____
- ○ _____
- ○ _____
- ○ _____

26 SATURDAY

_____
_____
_____
_____
_____
- ○ _____
- ○ _____
- ○ _____

27 SUNDAY

_____
_____
_____
_____
_____
- ○ _____
- ○ _____
- ○ _____

Notes and shit

_____
_____
_____

SEPTEMBER 2023

Sunday	Monday	Tuesday	Wednesday
August S M T W T F S 　 　 1 2 3 4 5 6 7 8 9 10 11 12 13 14 15 16 17 18 19 20 21 22 23 24 25 26 27 28 29 30 31	**October** S M T W T F S 1 2 3 4 5 6 7 8 9 10 11 12 13 14 15 16 17 18 19 20 21 22 23 24 25 26 27 28 29 30 31		
3	4 Labor Day (US, CA)	5	6
10	11 Patriot Day (US)	12	13
17	18	19	20
24 Yom Kippur begins at sundown	25	26	27

Damn, you're good

Thursday	Friday	Saturday	Important **shit**
	1	2	_____ _____ _____ _____ _____
7	8	9	_____ _____ _____ _____ _____
14	15 Rosh Hashanah begins at sundown	16	_____ _____ _____ _____
21	22 First Day of Fall	23	_____ _____ _____ _____
28	29	30	_____ _____ _____ _____ _____

28 MONDAY	29 TUESDAY	30 WEDNESDAY
Summer Bank Holiday (UK)		

28 MONDAY — Summer Bank Holiday (UK)

_____
_____
_____
_____
_____
_____
_____
_____
_____
_____
_____
_____

○ _____
○ _____
○ _____
○ _____
○ _____
○ _____
○ _____
○ _____
○ _____

29 TUESDAY

_____
_____
_____
_____
_____
_____
_____
_____
_____
_____
_____
_____

○ _____
○ _____
○ _____
○ _____
○ _____
○ _____
○ _____
○ _____
○ _____

30 WEDNESDAY

_____
_____
_____
_____
_____
_____
_____
_____
_____
_____
_____
_____

○ _____
○ _____
○ _____
○ _____
○ _____
○ _____
○ _____
○ _____
○ _____

Important as **fuck**

_____
_____
_____

Fucking grateful for...

_____
_____
_____

If only swearing burned calories

31 THURSDAY

_____
_____
_____
_____
_____
_____
_____
_____
_____
_____
_____
_____

- ○ _____
- ○ _____
- ○ _____
- ○ _____
- ○ _____
- ○ _____
- ○ _____
- ○ _____
- ○ _____

1 FRIDAY

_____
_____
_____
_____
_____
_____
_____
_____
_____
_____
_____
_____

- ○ _____
- ○ _____
- ○ _____
- ○ _____
- ○ _____
- ○ _____
- ○ _____
- ○ _____
- ○ _____

2 SATURDAY

_____
_____
_____
_____
_____

- ○ _____
- ○ _____
- ○ _____

3 SUNDAY

_____
_____
_____
_____
_____

- ○ _____
- ○ _____
- ○ _____

Notes and shit

_____
_____
_____

September 2023

4 MONDAY
Labor Day (US, CA)

_____
_____
_____
_____
_____
_____
_____
_____
_____
_____
_____
_____

○ _____
○ _____
○ _____
○ _____
○ _____
○ _____
○ _____
○ _____
○ _____

5 TUESDAY

_____
_____
_____
_____
_____
_____
_____
_____
_____
_____
_____
_____

○ _____
○ _____
○ _____
○ _____
○ _____
○ _____
○ _____
○ _____
○ _____

6 WEDNESDAY

_____
_____
_____
_____
_____
_____
_____
_____
_____
_____
_____
_____

○ _____
○ _____
○ _____
○ _____
○ _____
○ _____
○ _____
○ _____
○ _____

Important as **fuck**

_____
_____
_____

Fucking grateful for...

_____
_____
_____

Wake up. Kick ass. Repeat.

7 THURSDAY

_____
_____
_____
_____
_____
_____
_____
_____
_____
_____
_____
_____
_____
_____

- ○ _____
- ○ _____
- ○ _____
- ○ _____
- ○ _____
- ○ _____
- ○ _____
- ○ _____
- ○ _____

8 FRIDAY

_____
_____
_____
_____
_____
_____
_____
_____
_____
_____
_____
_____
_____
_____

- ○ _____
- ○ _____
- ○ _____
- ○ _____
- ○ _____
- ○ _____
- ○ _____
- ○ _____
- ○ _____

9 SATURDAY

_____
_____
_____
_____
_____
- ○ _____
- ○ _____
- ○ _____

10 SUNDAY

_____
_____
_____
_____
- ○ _____
- ○ _____
- ○ _____

Notes and shit

_____
_____
_____

September 2023

Important as **fuck**

Fucking grateful for...

Be the bitch you want to see in the world

14 THURSDAY

15 FRIDAY
Rosh Hashanah begins at sundown

16 SATURDAY

- ○
- ○
- ○

17 SUNDAY

14 THURSDAY tasks
- ○
- ○
- ○
- ○
- ○
- ○
- ○
- ○
- ○

15 FRIDAY tasks
- ○
- ○
- ○
- ○
- ○
- ○
- ○
- ○
- ○

17 SUNDAY tasks
- ○
- ○
- ○

Notes and **shit**

September 2023

18 MONDAY	19 TUESDAY	20 WEDNESDAY

○ _____ ○ _____ ○ _____
○ _____ ○ _____ ○ _____
○ _____ ○ _____ ○ _____
○ _____ ○ _____ ○ _____
○ _____ ○ _____ ○ _____
○ _____ ○ _____ ○ _____
○ _____ ○ _____ ○ _____
○ _____ ○ _____ ○ _____
○ _____ ○ _____ ○ _____

Important as **fuck**

Fucking grateful for...

You don't have to be perfect to be fucking amazing

21 THURSDAY

_____
_____
_____
_____
_____
_____
_____
_____
_____
_____
_____
_____
_____

○ _____
○ _____
○ _____
○ _____
○ _____
○ _____
○ _____
○ _____
○ _____

22 FRIDAY
First Day of Fall

_____
_____
_____
_____
_____
_____
_____
_____
_____
_____

○ _____
○ _____
○ _____
○ _____
○ _____
○ _____
○ _____
○ _____
○ _____

23 SATURDAY

_____
_____
_____
_____
_____

○ _____
○ _____
○ _____

24 SUNDAY
Yom Kippur begins at sundown

_____
_____
_____
_____
_____

○ _____
○ _____
○ _____

Notes and shit

_____
_____
_____

OCTOBER 2023

Sunday	Monday	Tuesday	Wednesday
1	2	3	4
8	9 Columbus Day (US) Thanksgiving (CA)	10	11
15	16	17	18
22	23	24	25
29	30	31 Halloween	

Do no harm, but take no shit

Thursday	Friday	Saturday	Important **shit**
5	6	7	_____
			_____
12	13	14	_____
			_____
19	20	21	_____
			_____
26	27	28	_____

September

S	M	T	W	T	F	S
					1	2
3	4	5	6	7	8	9
10	11	12	13	14	15	16
17	18	19	20	21	22	23
24	25	26	27	28	29	30

November

S	M	T	W	T	F	S
			1	2	3	4
5	6	7	8	9	10	11
12	13	14	15	16	17	18
19	20	21	22	23	24	25
26	27	28	29	30		

September-October 2023

25 MONDAY	26 TUESDAY	27 WEDNESDAY

Important as **fuck**

Fucking grateful for...

Two words, one finger

1 SUNDAY

Notes and shit

October 2023

2 MONDAY	3 TUESDAY	4 WEDNESDAY

_____
_____
_____
_____
_____
_____
_____
_____
_____
_____
_____

○ _____
○ _____
○ _____
○ _____
○ _____
○ _____
○ _____
○ _____
○ _____

Important as fuck

Fucking grateful for…

_____
_____
_____

People don't have to like it and you don't have to give a fuck

8 SUNDAY

Notes and **shit**

October 2023

Important as **fuck**

Fucking grateful for...

Save your fucks for important shit

12 THURSDAY

_____
_____
_____
_____
_____
_____
_____
_____
_____
_____
_____
_____

○ _____
○ _____
○ _____
○ _____
○ _____
○ _____
○ _____
○ _____
○ _____

13 FRIDAY

_____
_____
_____
_____
_____
_____
_____
_____
_____
_____

○ _____
○ _____
○ _____
○ _____
○ _____
○ _____
○ _____
○ _____
○ _____

14 SATURDAY

_____
_____
_____
_____
_____
_____
○ _____
○ _____
○ _____

15 SUNDAY

_____
_____
_____
_____
_____
○ _____
○ _____
○ _____

Notes and shit

_____
_____
_____

October 2023

16 MONDAY	17 TUESDAY	18 WEDNESDAY

Important as **fuck**

Fucking grateful for...

Be bold. Be brave. Be your badass self.

19 THURSDAY

_____
_____
_____
_____
_____
_____
_____
_____
_____
_____
_____

○ _____
○ _____
○ _____
○ _____
○ _____
○ _____
○ _____
○ _____
○ _____

20 FRIDAY

_____
_____
_____
_____
_____
_____
_____
_____
_____
_____

○ _____
○ _____
○ _____
○ _____
○ _____
○ _____
○ _____
○ _____
○ _____

21 SATURDAY

_____
_____
_____
_____
_____
○ _____
○ _____
○ _____

22 SUNDAY

_____
_____
_____
_____
_____
○ _____
○ _____
○ _____

Notes and **shit**

_____
_____
_____

October 2023

23 MONDAY   24 TUESDAY   25 WEDNESDAY

Important as **fuck**

Fucking grateful for...

Self care is fucking sanity, not vanity

26 THURSDAY

_____
_____
_____
_____
_____
_____
_____
_____
_____
_____
_____
_____
_____
○ _____
○ _____
○ _____
○ _____
○ _____
○ _____
○ _____
○ _____
○ _____

27 FRIDAY

_____
_____
_____
_____
_____
_____
_____
_____
_____
_____
_____
○ _____
○ _____
○ _____
○ _____
○ _____
○ _____
○ _____
○ _____
○ _____

28 SATURDAY

_____
_____
_____
_____
_____
_____
○ _____
○ _____
○ _____

29 SUNDAY

_____
_____
_____
_____
○ _____
○ _____
○ _____

Notes and **shit**

_____
_____
_____

NOVEMBER 2023

Sunday	Monday	Tuesday	Wednesday
October S M T W T F S 1 2 3 4 5 6 7 8 9 10 11 12 13 14 15 16 17 18 19 20 21 22 23 24 25 26 27 28 29 30 31	**December** S M T W T F S 1 2 3 4 5 6 7 8 9 10 11 12 13 14 15 16 17 18 19 20 21 22 23 24 25 26 27 28 29 30 31		**1**
5 Daylight Saving Time ends, Guy Fawkes Day (UK)	**6**	**7** Election Day (US)	**8**
12 Remembrance Sunday (UK)	**13**	**14**	**15**
19	**20**	**21**	**22**
26	**27**	**28**	**29**

A grateful heart is a magnet for more good shit

Thursday	Friday	Saturday	Important **shit**
2	3	4	_____
9	10	11 Veterans Day (US) Remembrance Day (CA)	
16	17	18	
23 Thanksgiving Day (US)	24	25	
30			

October-November 2023

Important as **fuck**

Fucking grateful for...

Fuck perfect

2 THURSDAY

_____
_____
_____
_____
_____
_____
_____
_____
_____
_____
_____
_____

- ◯ _____
- ◯ _____
- ◯ _____
- ◯ _____
- ◯ _____
- ◯ _____
- ◯ _____
- ◯ _____
- ◯ _____

3 FRIDAY

_____
_____
_____
_____
_____
_____
_____
_____
_____
_____

- ◯ _____
- ◯ _____
- ◯ _____
- ◯ _____
- ◯ _____
- ◯ _____
- ◯ _____
- ◯ _____
- ◯ _____

4 SATURDAY

_____
_____
_____
_____
_____

- ◯ _____
- ◯ _____
- ◯ _____

5 SUNDAY
Daylight Saving Time ends, Guy Fawkes Day (UK)

_____
_____
_____
_____
_____

- ◯ _____
- ◯ _____
- ◯ _____

Notes and shit

_____
_____
_____

November 2023

Important as **fuck**

Fucking grateful for...

Being under pressure is shit, but that's how diamonds are made

9 THURSDAY

_____
_____
_____
_____
_____
_____
_____
_____
_____
_____
_____
_____

○ _____
○ _____
○ _____
○ _____
○ _____
○ _____
○ _____
○ _____
○ _____

10 FRIDAY

_____
_____
_____
_____
_____
_____
_____
_____
_____

○ _____
○ _____
○ _____
○ _____
○ _____
○ _____
○ _____
○ _____
○ _____

11 SATURDAY
Veterans Day (US), Remembrance Day (CA)

_____
_____
_____
_____
_____

○ _____
○ _____
○ _____

12 SUNDAY
Remembrance Sunday (UK)

_____
_____
_____
_____
_____

○ _____
○ _____
○ _____

Notes and shit

_____
_____
_____

November 2023

In a world where you can be anything...

13 MONDAY	14 TUESDAY	15 WEDNESDAY

Important as **fuck**

Fucking grateful for...

Be kind. And kinda bitchy. You're only human after all.

16 THURSDAY

_____
_____
_____
_____
_____
_____
_____
_____
_____
_____
_____
_____
_____

○ _____
○ _____
○ _____
○ _____
○ _____
○ _____
○ _____
○ _____
○ _____

17 FRIDAY

_____
_____
_____
_____
_____
_____
_____
_____
_____
_____
_____
_____

○ _____
○ _____
○ _____
○ _____
○ _____
○ _____
○ _____
○ _____
○ _____

18 SATURDAY

_____
_____
_____
_____
_____
_____
○ _____
○ _____
○ _____

19 SUNDAY

_____
_____
_____
_____
_____
○ _____
○ _____
○ _____

Notes and shit

_____
_____
_____

November 2023

20 MONDAY	21 TUESDAY	22 WEDNESDAY

Important as **fuck**

Fucking grateful for...

If swearing is bad, why do they call it strong language?

23 THURSDAY
Thanksgiving Day (US)

_____
_____
_____
_____
_____
_____
_____
_____
_____
_____
_____
_____

○ _____
○ _____
○ _____
○ _____
○ _____
○ _____
○ _____
○ _____
○ _____

24 FRIDAY

_____
_____
_____
_____
_____
_____
_____
_____
_____

○ _____
○ _____
○ _____
○ _____
○ _____
○ _____
○ _____
○ _____
○ _____

25 SATURDAY

_____
_____
_____
_____
_____
○ _____
○ _____
○ _____

26 SUNDAY

_____
_____
_____
_____
_____
○ _____
○ _____
○ _____

Notes and shit

_____
_____
_____

DECEMBER 2023

Sunday	Monday	Tuesday	Wednesday
November S M T W T F S 　　　1 2 3 4 5 6 7 8 9 10 11 12 13 14 15 16 17 18 19 20 21 22 23 24 25 26 27 28 29 30	January 2024 S M T W T F S 　1 2 3 4 5 6 7 8 9 10 11 12 13 14 15 16 17 18 19 20 21 22 23 24 25 26 27 28 29 30 31		
3	4	5	6
10	11	12	13
17	18	19	20
24	25 Christmas Day	26 Kwanzaa begins (US) Boxing Day (UK, CA)	27
31 New Year's Eve			

Fuckity fuck fuck, fuckity fuck fuck, watch that fuckery go

Thursday	Friday	Saturday	Important **shit**
	1	2	_____ _____ _____ _____ _____
7 Hanukkah begins at sundown	8	9	_____ _____ _____ _____
14	15	16	_____ _____ _____ _____
21 First Day of Winter	22	23	_____ _____ _____ _____
28	29	30	_____ _____ _____ _____
			_____ _____ _____ _____

November-December 2023

Important as **fuck**

Fucking grateful for...

It's beginning to look a lot like fuck this

30 THURSDAY

_____
_____
_____
_____
_____
_____
_____
_____
_____
_____
_____
_____

- ○ _____
- ○ _____
- ○ _____
- ○ _____
- ○ _____
- ○ _____
- ○ _____
- ○ _____
- ○ _____

1 FRIDAY

_____
_____
_____
_____
_____
_____
_____
_____
_____
_____
_____

- ○ _____
- ○ _____
- ○ _____
- ○ _____
- ○ _____
- ○ _____
- ○ _____
- ○ _____
- ○ _____

2 SATURDAY

_____
_____
_____
_____
_____
- ○ _____
- ○ _____
- ○ _____

3 SUNDAY

_____
_____
_____
_____
_____
_____
- ○ _____
- ○ _____
- ○ _____

Notes and shit

_____
_____
_____

December 2023

4 MONDAY	5 TUESDAY	6 WEDNESDAY

Important as **fuck**

Fucking grateful for...

Have a fucktastic day

7 THURSDAY
Hanukkah begins at sundown

_____
_____
_____
_____
_____
_____
_____
_____
_____
_____
_____
_____
_____

- ◯ _____
- ◯ _____
- ◯ _____
- ◯ _____
- ◯ _____
- ◯ _____
- ◯ _____
- ◯ _____
- ◯ _____

8 FRIDAY

_____
_____
_____
_____
_____
_____
_____
_____
_____
_____
_____
_____
_____

- ◯ _____
- ◯ _____
- ◯ _____
- ◯ _____
- ◯ _____
- ◯ _____
- ◯ _____
- ◯ _____
- ◯ _____

9 SATURDAY

_____
_____
_____
_____
_____
_____
- ◯ _____
- ◯ _____
- ◯ _____

10 SUNDAY

_____
_____
_____
_____
_____
- ◯ _____
- ◯ _____
- ◯ _____

Notes and shit

_____
_____
_____

December 2023

11 MONDAY	12 TUESDAY	13 WEDNESDAY
_____	_____	_____
_____	_____	_____
_____	_____	_____
_____	_____	_____
_____	_____	_____
_____	_____	_____
_____	_____	_____
_____	_____	_____
_____	_____	_____
_____	_____	_____
_____	_____	_____
_____	_____	_____
○ _____	○ _____	○ _____
○ _____	○ _____	○ _____
○ _____	○ _____	○ _____
○ _____	○ _____	○ _____
○ _____	○ _____	○ _____
○ _____	○ _____	○ _____
○ _____	○ _____	○ _____
○ _____	○ _____	○ _____
○ _____	○ _____	○ _____

Important as **fuck**

Fucking grateful for...

_____

_____

_____

look at you kicking ass and shit

14 THURSDAY

_____
_____
_____
_____
_____
_____
_____
_____
_____
_____
_____
_____
_____

- ○ _____
- ○ _____
- ○ _____
- ○ _____
- ○ _____
- ○ _____
- ○ _____
- ○ _____
- ○ _____

15 FRIDAY

_____
_____
_____
_____
_____
_____
_____
_____
_____
_____

- ○ _____
- ○ _____
- ○ _____
- ○ _____
- ○ _____
- ○ _____
- ○ _____
- ○ _____
- ○ _____

16 SATURDAY

_____
_____
_____
_____
_____

- ○ _____
- ○ _____
- ○ _____

17 SUNDAY

_____
_____
_____
_____
_____

- ○ _____
- ○ _____
- ○ _____

Notes and shit

_____
_____
_____

December 2023

18 MONDAY	19 TUESDAY	20 WEDNESDAY

Important as **fuck**

Fucking grateful for...

Here's a good New Year's resolution: unfollow assholes

21 THURSDAY
First Day of Winter

_____
_____
_____
_____
_____
_____
_____
_____
_____
_____
_____
_____
_____
○ _____
○ _____
○ _____
○ _____
○ _____
○ _____
○ _____
○ _____
○ _____

22 FRIDAY

_____
_____
_____
_____
_____
_____
_____
_____
_____
_____
_____
○ _____
○ _____
○ _____
○ _____
○ _____
○ _____
○ _____
○ _____
○ _____

23 SATURDAY

_____
_____
_____
_____
_____
○ _____
○ _____
○ _____

24 SUNDAY
Christmas Eve

_____
_____
_____
_____
○ _____
○ _____
○ _____

Notes and shit

_____
_____
_____

December 2023

Important as **fuck**

Fucking grateful for...

You are amazing as fuck. Keep that shit up.

28 THURSDAY

_____
_____
_____
_____
_____
_____
_____
_____
_____
_____
_____
_____
_____
_____
_____

○ _____
○ _____
○ _____
○ _____
○ _____
○ _____
○ _____
○ _____
○ _____

29 FRIDAY

_____
_____
_____
_____
_____
_____
_____
_____
_____
_____
_____
_____
_____
_____

○ _____
○ _____
○ _____
○ _____
○ _____
○ _____
○ _____
○ _____
○ _____

30 SATURDAY

_____
_____
_____
_____
_____
_____
○ _____
○ _____
○ _____

31 SUNDAY
New Year's Eve

_____
_____
_____
_____
_____
_____
○ _____
○ _____
○ _____

Notes and shit

_____
_____

My Brilliant Thoughts & Shit

My Brilliant Thoughts & Shit

My Brilliant Thoughts & Shit

My Brilliant Thoughts & Shit

My Brilliant Thoughts & Shit

Thank you for trying us out

A favor please

Would you take a quick minute to leave us a rating/review on Amazon? It makes a *HUGE* difference and we would really appreciate it!

More Fun From Sassy Quotes Press

See these and more at
amazon.com/author/sassyquotespress

**Or scan this QR code
with your device**

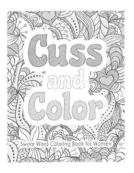

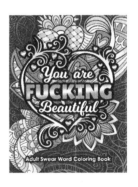

Made in the USA
Las Vegas, NV
07 January 2023

65125942R20079